Big Max
A TRUE STORY

by Karen McDonald

To Jack
& Georgia—

Karen
McDonald

ISBN: 978-0-578-34724-0 (Ebook)
ISBN: 978-1-957255-02-6 (Paperback)

Illustrated by Marlon at GetYourBookIllustrations
www.getyourbookillustrations.com

First Print 2022

To G-our Big Mac Snack Attack

Hi! I'm **Big Max**.
I'm a mixed breed.

I am a mix between a Great Dane and a Labrador.
My breed is called the Gentle Giant because we are as
big as a baby horse but as gentle as a kitten.

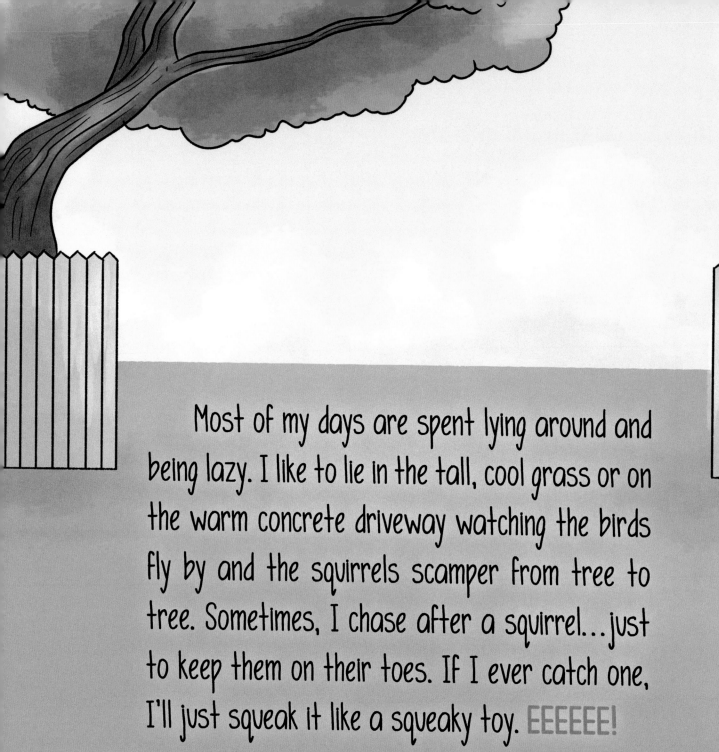

Most of my days are spent lying around and being lazy. I like to lie in the tall, cool grass or on the warm concrete driveway watching the birds fly by and the squirrels scamper from tree to tree. Sometimes, I chase after a squirrel...just to keep them on their toes. If I ever catch one, I'll just squeak it like a squeaky toy. EEEEEE!

I live with my humans: Papa G and Mama K. I've got them trained. Papa G passes out treats like Halloween candy! I call him Big Mac Snack Attack. He keeps treats in the garage, the laundry room, the pantry, and the big refrigerator! I follow him around like a puppy.

At breakfast, I lie at his feet waiting for flour tortillas. Papa G rolls one like a burrito, then gently lays it in my mouth. I bite it, then swallow it...whole. **DELICIOUS!** I wish he would let me eat the whole bag!

Late at night, Papa G and I even share vanilla ice cream from the same big spoon. My warm mouth cools down as the cold, sweet ice cream melts and slides down into my belly. **YUM!**

However, belly rubs are better than tortillas or ice cream. Have you ever had one? Mama K is a sucker when she sees me in "Belly Mode." Belly Mode is when you lie on your back and stretch your front paws and back paws out in opposite directions like a rubber band. Mama K always stops what she's doing, then kneels to rub my belly and scratch my booty while she talks sweetly to me. Her voice is like music to my ears. I try to get at least 5 belly rubs a day. You should try one, too.

I have a good life now, but it didn't start off so well. My previous human was not kind to me. He hurt me and crushed my front left shoulder. The police came to help and ordered him to release me to an animal shelter. He dropped me off at a dog rescue when I was eleven months old. The kind people took me to a vet, and he told them I would need to have my front left leg amputated. They put me up for adoption but were afraid no one would want me.

Then I met Papa G and Mama K.
They wanted me! They adopted me!
They loved me, but. . . I was very hard to love.
I didn't know what love was.
I didn't know these humans yet and I was
afraid they would be like my last one.

They tried to **kennel** me at night, but I refused to go in the cage. They bought me a bigger kennel and held tasty treats out to encourage me, but I am **SUPER** stubborn and refused to go in it, too.

Exhausted and frustrated, they let me sleep wherever I wanted. . . which was on the c-shaped, leather couch in the den. Climbing up on it was hard, but once I got my big body up there, I melted into the soft leather like a baseball fits into a baseball glove.

Papa G and Mama K had to leave each morning to go to work, which gave me lots of time to explore. I followed my nose across the driveway and over to the long wooden fence. I found 25 baby jasmine plants that smelled like sweet lollipops! Papa G had just planted them. I leaned my big nose closer in to get a whiff.

HMMM...Sweetness drifted up my nose and tickled my brain. My lips slightly grazed a small, green leaf.

Nibble, Nibble.
Then my big mouth attacked the bush, shredding it into tiny, wooden toothpicks!

YIKES! I kicked the dirt around on the driveway trying to hide my big mess, then I limped back inside for a nap.

I was too tired to crawl up on the couch, so I lay down in the big, fluffy pillow on the floor next to the couch in the den. I curled up in it like a cat in a cat bed. Then I drifted off to sleep, dreaming of sweet baby jasmine leaves.

I was awakened by Papa G's truck driving up the long driveway. Quickly, I jumped up and limped out of the laundry room doggy door to greet him, hoping to distract him from my big mess. He stopped his truck, opened the door, and reached down to pet my big head. Stepping out of the truck, he bent down to give me a big, wet kiss on the lips. I **LOVE** big, wet kisses on the lips!

"Big Max," he said sadly, "What happened? It looks like you got into a boxing match with one of my baby jasmine. Big Max, I love you, but you can't eat the plants!" I leaned my big head into his pants, and he rubbed my big, soft ears. I wanted him to know I was sorry. I followed him to the garage, where he gave me a tasty chicken treat. Big Mac Snack Attack had forgiven me.

Papa G left again. I was bored.
Following my nose, I found a big closet.

Sniff. Sniff. Sniff.

My super sniffer stopped at a pair of boots.
Gently biting the toe of a boot, I pulled it to the
floor, where I rested my head on it for a minute,
letting the leather smell waft up my nose.
Wet, slimy drool began to leak out of my mouth
onto the tile floor. As the drool puddled, my
heart longed for a tiny taste of the boot.
My brain quit working and my teeth took
over, demolishing the toe of the boot.
I knew I would be in big trouble now.
Dropping the chewed boot on the hallway floor,
I limped back to the warm driveway to lie down and wait.

Papa G drove up the long driveway and parked his truck. As he walked by me, he said, **"Do you want a treat?"** Pushing myself up, I followed Big Mac Snack Attack into the house and to the laundry room. I gently took a tasty chicken treat from his hand, then slid down on the hard tile floor to eat it, forgetting all about the boot. **YUM!**

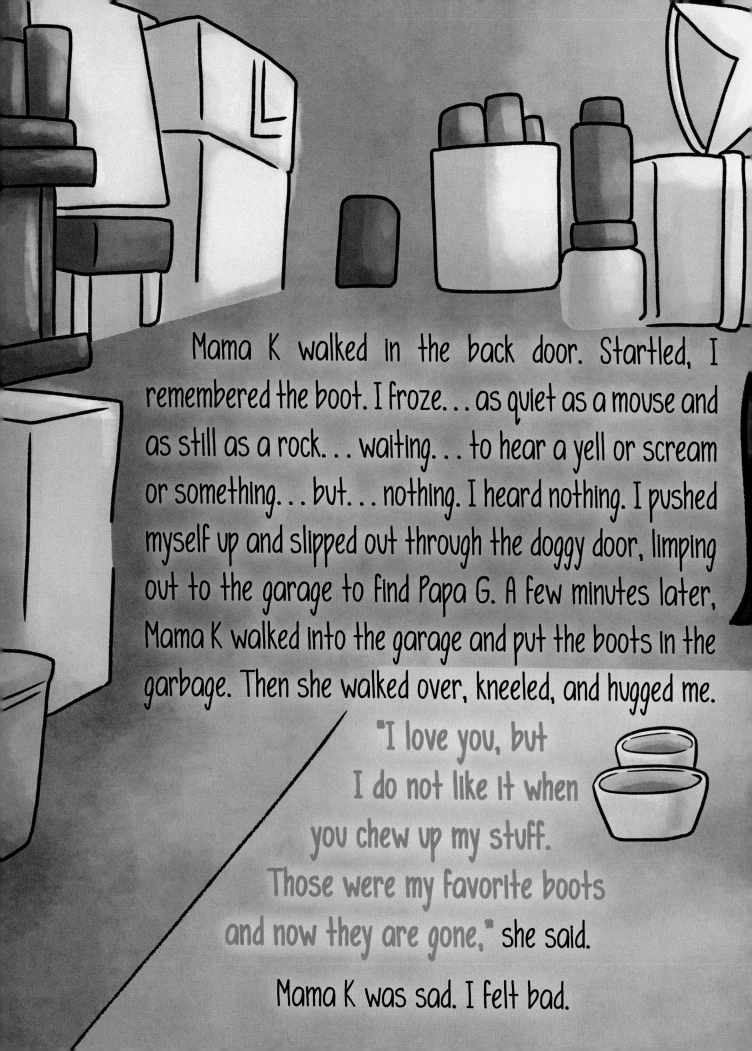

Mama K walked in the back door. Startled, I remembered the boot. I froze... as quiet as a mouse and as still as a rock... waiting... to hear a yell or scream or something... but... nothing. I heard nothing. I pushed myself up and slipped out through the doggy door, limping out to the garage to find Papa G. A few minutes later, Mama K walked into the garage and put the boots in the garbage. Then she walked over, kneeled, and hugged me.

"I love you, but I do not like it when you chew up my stuff. Those were my favorite boots and now they are gone," she said.

Mama K was sad. I felt bad.

Walking every day seemed to help my shoulder. I walked slowly, limping with each step, but Mama K didn't mind my slow pace. She just held my red leash and talked to me as we listened to the birds chatter and the squirrels squeak.

Timez

I wanted to make better choices. However, I still refused to kennel and I was having a hard time with self-control.

Eventually, I ate **ALL** of Papa G's baby jasmine plants. I chewed up magazines, books, pillows, plastic buckets, a water hose, many sprinkler heads, and sticks.

Mama K and Papa G never got mad at me, but I knew they were sad and frustrated. They would just say, "Big Max, we love you, but we do not love your choices. Please, stop eating things."

At night, I patrolled the property. "I am Big Max," I barked, letting all nocturnal animals know I was on guard duty. I surveyed my kingdom with my eyes wide open, my ears on alert, and my teeth ready to taste things that needed to be tested to be sure they were safe.

I walked inside and outside, upstairs and down, out to the garage and over to the grassy hill. I circled the swimming pool and stopped for a quick drink, being careful not to get too close for fear I might fall in. My super sniffer led me to curious new smells.

First, I tasted the corner of a brown leather chair in the living room, taking one **BIG** bite! "Too tough and too hard to chew!" I thought as I spit it out. Next, I tasted the seat of a tall, iron chair, but the fur got stuck in my teeth! I shook my lips trying to get the cowhide out of my teeth. Then, I bit the head off a wooden duck that was staring at me with his yellow, beady eyes that glowed in the dark. After that, I attacked a deer in the corner of our living room that was frozen by the light of the full moon. I bit his nose off! Then, I chewed up the rug at the back door so no one would trip over it. Finally, our house felt safe.

On Saturday, Mama K took me to the vet to have my front left shoulder x-rayed. A small, white, fluffy dog was sitting on the floor. She whined. As her mama picked her up, she stuck her nose up in the air and looked the other way. Next, I saw a big German Shepherd wearing a vest. He looked like he was in training for something important.

I tried to give him a booty bump as I walked past him, but he acted like he didn't see me. Then, a long, brown wiener dog ran out of a room and right under my belly! He was shaking all over. He barked, "Don't go in that room with four walls and a door. Bad things happened in there!"

Mama K sat down on a bench, and I sat on the hard tile floor next to her. My paws slipped out in front of me, leaving me flat on the floor. We waited. I wanted to go into Belly Mode, but I was afraid. Finally, it was our turn.

As we walked into our room, a lady walked in through a back door. She hooked a leash up to my collar and led me out. I was nervous. She took me to a machine that flashed bright lights. Then, she returned me to the room where I limped over to Mama K. A man in a white coat walked in. I leaned into Mama K's leg for protection, and she gently rubbed my head. The man told her my front left shoulder was damaged. Before they amputated it, he wanted to try a steroid shot. He leaned down and pinched my front left shoulder. "BARK!! BARK!!! BARK!!!" I barked as loudly as I could to let him know that hurt!

Driving up the long driveway, I saw Papa G waiting for us. He opened the back door of the jeep and helped me walk down the ramp. It felt like I was walking a tight rope. I followed him into the garage. Big Mac Snack Attack gave me **TWO** treats because Mama K told him I was a "*good boy*" when I got the steroid shot. Then he leaned over and gave me a big, wet kiss on the lips! Yum!

That night, I couldn't sleep. My shoulder hurt. I couldn't get comfortable on the couch or in my big, fluffy dog pillow. I wandered around the house listening for noises. I limped into the living room. My big, black body rubbed up against the fancy crushed velvet couch. I knew the fancy crushed velvet couch was "off limits" to me, but it felt like a feather. . . gently touching my fur! So, I pulled myself up onto it and fell asleep.

I had a bad, bad dream...the man in the long, white coat was chasing me around the room with four walls! Bright lights were flashing on and off! The room started to spin! Then I woke up! I couldn't believe my eyes. The fancy crushed velvet couch was "POOFED!" Scraps of brown velvet littered the floor and white stuffing poured out of a humongous hole in the back cushion. Trouble was on the horizon. I high tailed it out of there, zooming through the laundry room doggy door. I limped as fast as I could down the long driveway to the garage, where I found a perfect hiding spot behind the long, green couch.

The long, green couch is one of my favorite couches on my turf. The seat is low to the ground, which helps me pull myself up onto it. However, the cushions are so super soft that my body melts into them like quicksand. Terrified of my future, I feared that if I crawled up onto the couch, I would not be able to make a fast escape. So, I stayed hidden behind the couch and waited.

Nothing.

Nothing? Were my ears turned on? No screaming? No yelling? No nothing? "Wait a minute," I thought. They haven't seen it yet.

I peeked around the end of the green couch. The coast was clear. So, I slowly limped back into the house through the bedroom doggy door to see if Mama K and Papa G were still sleeping. The big bed was made. No humans in sight.

Wait!!! What was that smell? Bacon? My stomach started to rumble. My mouth started to water. I tiptoed through the living room past the "POOFED" couch. Oh my, that fancy couch was not so fancy anymore! Quickly, I slipped around the corner, trying to be invisible, which is kind of hard when you are a Gentle Giant! Drool was seeping out of my lips as I snuck closer to the kitchen. Papa G and Mama K were sitting at the table. I slithered up next to Papa G and laid my head on his foot and waited. Drool was collecting on the floor. At last, Big Mac Snack Attack held a piece of bacon under my nose. Slowly, I opened my big mouth and gently took the bacon from his fingers. Happy thoughts filled my head as the warm, crispy bacon filled my mouth. I licked my lips with my long, pink tongue and thought, "This is going to be a good day."

Later that afternoon while I was snoozing in the tall, cool grass, Papa G drove up the long driveway in his truck. It was Big Mac Snack Attack time! Pulling myself up, I limped over to greet him as he stepped out of the truck. He walked to the back of his truck and pulled out a huge bundle of orange plastic. "What were we going to do with that?" I wondered. Papa G rolled it across the garage opening and nailed it to the walls. Then he took another long piece and rolled it across the other garage opening and nailed one end closed. He tied the other end to a pole. This was cool. Papa G made us a Man Cave! No one could come in and no one could go out!

We could hang out in the garage together. . . all day, just the two of us, best buddies. . . Big Max and Papa G!

That night, Papa G walked me out to the garage. . . to our Man Cave. "Big Max," he said, "Mama K and I love you very much, but we are not happy with your choices. It was not okay for you to "POOF" the living room couch. From now on, you will have to sleep out here in the garage."

Mama K walked out to the garage and gave me a big hug and a belly rub, but then they both walked away, leaving me all alone in the garage with the orange wall. "Well, at least I have the long, green couch," I thought. I climbed up on it and slipped off to sleep.

Scary noises woke me up in the middle of the night. I wasn't used to sleeping alone in the dark wilderness of the garage. Ugh! I didn't like being alone. I was afraid. I wanted Mama K or Papa G to come sleep out here with me. I started barking and barking. . . but no one came. Finally, I fell back asleep. When I woke up, I saw that a cushion from the green couch had been "POOFED!" Oh, no. . . I did it again!

Papa G walked out to the garage. He rolled the big orange wall back and walked in. "Big Max," he said, "What happened?" Papa G stuffed the stuffing back into the pillow cushion and wrapped duct tape over the hole. He put the cushion back on the couch and said,

"Big Max, I love you but this needs to stop! You are eating everything that is not nailed down! STOP! PLEASE! We need you to make better choices!"

Then he leaned down and gave me kisses. Feeling loved, I laid down at his feet and fell asleep.

Mama K walked out to the garage and saw the duct tape on the green couch. "Big Max," she said as she kneeled down next to me and started scratching my head and ears, "What are we going to do with you?" I rolled over into Belly Mode. It felt good to be loved.

The next day, I did not feel the love. I was bored. I figured out how to pull the pole out of the hole in the garage floor that held up the orange wall. Then I walked around patrolling my territory, but sadly, there was no action. So, I climbed up on the couch in the den, when a storm rolled over our house. The bottom fell out of the clouds. Lightning lit up the sky and thunder roared, rattling the windows. I am EXTREMELY scared of loud noises. I tried to bury myself into the cushions, but I couldn't get under them. They kept flipping off the couch onto the floor. Next, I tried to chew through the bottom of the couch to get under it, but the springs were too hard to chew.

Quickly, I jumped off the couch, bumping the coffee table, which sent Mama K's favorite hand painted Indian bowl crashing to the floor, shattering into a thousand pieces.

CRASH!
KABOOM!!

The thunder wouldn't stop. So, I ran around the couch, bumping into the tall bookshelf, knocking a few picture frames to the floor. They shattered. I leaped up into the air trying not to cut my big paws on the glass. I landed on the wooden floor sliding into my big kennel, which crashed into a table, knocking over a bear lamp. I pulled my body up and limped to the big closet. Finally, I curled up in a ball in a corner under Papa G's pants and waited for the storm to pass.

Papa G came home and found the den a disaster. I heard him call Mama K and say, "I wanted to give you a heads up because you are not going to be happy with Big Max when you get home."

"Why?" Mama K asked.

"Because the den is a disaster," Papa G replied, walking out to the garage.

I wanted to follow him. I knew he would understand and give me a big, wet kiss on the lips and a Big Mac Snack Attack snack, but I stayed frozen. I figured that was probably the best place to lie low, stay hidden, and keep out of the way.

I heard the back door open. My ears perked up. Listening. . . I heard Mama K crying. My heart broke. I knew I made a few wrong choices. . . again, but some of it was an accident. If she only knew the whole story, she would understand. I slipped out through the bedroom doggy door and limped to the garage to find Papa G.

Papa G was sitting at his desk. "Big Max, what happened?" he asked. I walked up to him, lying my big head in his lap. I was sorry I made the big mess in the den. Papa G just rubbed my big head. Then he gave me a chicken treat followed by lots of kisses. I hoped Mama K would be that understanding too.

The next day, Papa G took me for a ride in his truck. We stopped at a big building. The sign said, "**Dog Grooming and Boarding**." Papa G stepped out of the truck, clipped my leash onto my collar, and walked me inside. I liked this place. There were a lot of good smells. I perked my ears up. I heard lots of barking in the distance. Then I heard the man tell Papa G to come back in 10 days. 10 Days? What did that mean? I wanted to know, but Papa G just handed my leash to the man, leaned down and gave me a big kiss on my lips, then walked away.

"Hi, Big Max," the man said. "Let's get you settled in." He walked me to a large kennel. I limped in. I noticed there was a bowl of water and a large, rectangle, blue bed that looked a little bit like a hammock. I walked over and laid down. It felt like I was sleeping on a cloud, weightless. I liked my new bed, but I wasn't sure I liked my new home.

The man came by my kennel later. He hooked up my leash, and we went for another walk. He showed me around the property. We stopped at a giant fenced in area full of dogs running around a big pond. He walked me in and unhooked my leash. I limped over to the pond and swam around for a minute.

The cool water felt refreshing, but my shoulder was really hurting, so I pulled myself out. I limped over to a grassy knoll and lay down in the shade of a big oak tree. I watched the other dogs run and play. I wanted to run and play with them. Later that afternoon, the man came back, hooked up my leash, and walked me to my kennel. I was sad to be in the kennel alone. I missed Papa G and Mama K. I wanted to go home.

For nine days, the man came to my kennel and took me for a walk. We would end up at the giant field with the big pond, where he would let me off my leash. I would limp around until I found the perfect place to rest for the afternoon. I needed the warm, hard ground to heat up my front left shoulder to make it feel better. I missed Mama K's daily belly rubs and Papa G's kisses. I missed Big Mac Snack Attacks and the green couch in the garage. I missed the long driveway where I stood guard looking for squirrels to chase. But most of all, I missed my family, Papa G and Mama K. We were a family.

I thought back through my days with them and realized even when I did not make the right choices, they still loved me. They were always there for me. I longed to be with them again.

On the tenth day, the man came, hooked up my leash, and walked me to the front of the building. This wasn't our normal walk. He hooked my leash under the counter, and then he walked behind the counter. I sat down. My front paws slid out from under me on the hard, cold tile floor. . . **plop!** I lay my head down, resting it on my front paws. I wondered why the man had brought me here. Then, the front door opened.

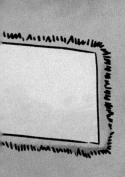

I glanced up with my round, black eyes...**Papa G!!! Papa G was back!!!** I slipped and slid trying to get up on all four paws as fast as I could. I could not believe my eyes. Papa G was back! He walked straight up to me and bent down, giving me lots of kisses! "This must be Day 10," I thought. **"This must be the Best Day Ever!"** I was so excited to see Papa G! He thanked the man, grabbed my leash, and we walked out to his truck. He helped me climb up into the backseat, where I lay down. As Papa G drove, I hoped we were going home.

I could feel it in my bones... we were driving up our long driveway. I pushed my big body up on my front paws and looked out the window. I was home! I was home!

Mama K came running out the back door. Papa G stopped his truck and helped me climb out. Mama K ran over and dropped to her knees. She threw her arms around my big, black body and squeezed me tight. I gave her lots of kisses, then I rolled over into Belly Mode and got the best belly rub ever!

I was home. I was with my family. We were together. "This is what love feels like," I thought.

That night, Papa G and Mama K tried to get me to kennel. I wouldn't. I don't know why... but I just couldn't. So, I slept on the green couch in the garage with the orange wall.

The next day, there were more holes in the green couch cushions. Mama K and Papa G just stuffed the white stuffing back inside the holes and put duct tape on them. I don't know why I kept eating the green couch, but I did. However, I got better. Papa G and Mama K noticed I ate less and less of the green couch until one day I quit eating it all together. In fact, I **didn't bite or eat anything anymore.** I knew Mama K and Papa G loved me, I knew I was home, and **I knew I was safe.**

No more orange wall. I got to sleep anywhere I wanted...

...except for the fancy crushed velvet couch that had been fixed and was still off limits!

It's been three years now. I still limp and I always will. However, I have built up muscle mass around my shoulder joint, and hopefully I will never need to have my left leg amputated. Belly Mode, Big Mac Snack Attack, kisses, and chasing squirrels are my favorite daily activities. I'm still **VERY** scared of loud noises, and I will run and hide, but I know Mama K and Papa G will always love me and keep me safe.

P.S. Papa G bought me my own doggy van! This must be my best day ever!

Karen & Big Max

Thanks for reading Big Max!

Please leave a review.

Big Max's instagram: bigmaxgentlegiant

My website: karenmcdonaldauthor.com